Gold Cup

Bowler Hat

Also available in this series:
Spot What!
Spot What! Amazing
Spot What! Spectacular
Spot What! Magical
Spot What! Metropolis

Published by Hinkler Books Pty Ltd
45–55 Fairchild Street
Heatherton Victoria 3202 Australia
www.hinkler.com.au

hinkler

Authors: Nick Bryant and Rowan Summers
Cover design: Nick Bryant
Spot What logo design: Peter Tovey
Illustrations: Dynamo Limited
Prepress: Graphic Print Group

Images © Shutterstock.com: Retro circus poster with elephant performing on ball © olillia; Vintage circus poster with seal playing with ball © olillia; Set of characters of yellow emoticons © Vertes Edmond Mihai's; Cartoon vegetables and fruits © Virinaflora; Unusual cloud over sea © Fedorov Oleksiy; Rough blue holiday cover with many snowflakes © Krivosheev Vitaly; Gold yellow background retro striped layout, pale abstract © Apostrophe; Vector set of heraldic animals © Genestro; Playing card back side 60x90 mm © bobyramone; Old playing card (jack) © Micha Klootwijk; Cartoon fruit set © Pushkin; Corn symbol © Tribalium; Peacock raise his feathers © elmm.

ISBN: 978 1 7436 3271 0

Printed and bound in China

Bagpipes

Noise Maker

Abacus

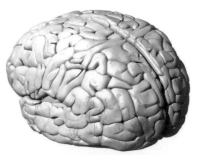

Brain

Banjo

Contents

Christmas Bauble

Doctor's Bag

Stagecoach

Lei

Camel

Hip, hip, hooray! The carnival!
Come and see the grand parade!
Find a crocodile, a cabbage, a kitten,
A hedgehog and pink lemonade.

Can you spot a warm fur coat,
Three bowling pins, a joker,
A crystal ball, a bulldog,
A xylophone, a fire poker?

The carousel goes around,
The riders all go up and down.
Can you spot a salt shaker,
A knife, a fork, a pen, a crown?

Can you find a unicorn,
A moose, a goose, a snake,
An ostrich and a teacup,
A seahorse, boat and rake?

The Ferris wheel, around we go,
Not too fast and not too slow.
Can you spot a stagecoach,
A top, a tap and falling snow?

Can you find a bucket, a drum,
A flute and three robots,
A watering can, a camel,
An egg and two teapots?

CARNIVAL

COMPANY

Now it's time to test your skill,
With sideshow fun and games to thrill!
Find a camera, a cushion, a gnome,
A typewriter and a daffodil.

Can you spot a candy cane,
A bowling ball, a sailing ship,
Some knitting and a brush,
A canary and a paperclip?

Can you spot an elephant,
Three butterflies, a hare,
A pumpkin, a rhinoceros,
An owl, a bull, a bear?

Can you find a toucan,
Four jungle cats, a dog,
A witch, a watch, a walrus,
A sheep, two flies and a frog?

SPOT WHAT

The rollercoaster rushes past,
Up and down and up again.
Find a kite and three ship's masts,
A vintage car, a plane, a train.

Can you spot a rollerskate,
A covered wagon and a bat,
Three shoes, a ladder and a crate,
A tub, two ducks, a bowler hat?

15

Come and ride the bumper cars,
Get ready, set, and off they go!
Find a yoyo, a slipper, a snail,
Two skunks, a leopard and a bow.

Can you spot four stop signs,
Six arrows and a racing flag,
A hovercraft, three lightning bolts,
A golden cup and a doctor's bag?

Balloons, balloons, balloons for sale!
Can you find a dragon, a whale,
A ticket, a pig, a goldfish, a mouse,
A bunch of flowers and a little house?

Can you spot five silver stars,
A cat, a fiddle, a spoon,
A wasp, a blimp, a tomato,
The sun, the Earth and the moon?

Time to stop and have a break,
A little rest and a snack.
Can you spot five hotdogs,
Three hamburgers, five sacks?

Can you find a banana,
Five lollipops and a lemon,
An ear of corn, four cherries,
A cockroach, a watermelon?

SPOT
WHAT

POOL RULES

Come on the boatride,
To lands far away!
Can you spot a rocket,
A turtle, a deer, a sleigh?

Can you find a toothbrush,
Six moths, a dollar bill,
The flags of eight nations,
A pillow, a ruler, a quill?

Many things are lost and found,
Left on rides or on the ground.
Can you spot a steering wheel,
A shoe, a skull, a banana peel?

Can you find three dominoes,
Two dice and a music box,
Some teeth, a spanner, a pickle,
Seven coins, a pair of socks?

Come inside the house of FUN,
There are plenty of laughs for you!
Find a budgerigar, a ram,
A chest, a rose, a kangaroo.

Can you spot some bagpipes,
A refrigerator, a whistle,
A pogo stick, a handkerchief,
A queen, a Scottish thistle?

CARNIVAL

See if you can spot these things in every picture:

Can you find the words SPOT WHAT,
A monkey, a peacock,
A baseball, an umbrella,
A doughnut and a clock?

Doughnut

Peacock

Monkey

Rules For The Spot What Game

1. Flip a coin to see who goes first. The winner of the coin toss is the 'caller' and the other player is the 'spotter'.

2. The caller chooses a page from the book and picks an item for the spotter to find, saying, for example, 'Can you spot a jack-in-the-box?'

3. The spotter must then try to find the item on the page.

4. If the spotter can't find it, the caller gets 5 points and shows the spotter where it is and has another turn.

5. If the spotter can find the item, then he or she gets 5 points and now it's his or her turn to be the caller.

6. The first to reach 30 points wins but you could also set your own limit or simply play best out of three!

You can make the game more challenging by putting a time limit of one to three minutes on each search. Try making up your own games too!

Baseball

Clock

Umbrella

The Spot What Challenge

The following items are much harder to find,
so get ready for the challenge!

Robot

Joker

Parade
(pages 4/5)

A ruler
A pencil
A lawnmower
A pair of cowboy boots
A bow tie
5 silver stars
4 different fruits
A rhinoceros

Wheel
(pages 8/9)

A record
A pair of crutches
A sled
5 cars
A thermometer
A pyramid
3 matchsticks
2 knots

Carousel
(pages 6/7)

A motorbike
A guitar
A goat
A jack-o'-lantern
2 diving helmets
A turtle
A teddy bear
A knight

Knitting

Sideshows
(pages 10/11)

A white rose
A royal flush
A cat
A monocle
A crystal ball
A rollerskate
A brain
A licence plate

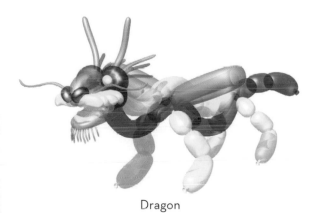

Dragon

Unicorn

Hedgehog

Jack-O'-Lantern

Masks
(pages 12/13)

A penguin
Pinocchio
4 pairs of glasses
Comedy and Tragedy
5 skeletons
A giraffe
Tutankhamun
A bolt

Bumper
(pages 16/17)

An 8-ball
A pumpkin
A bowling ball
A hairbrush
A fishing rod
A banjo
A feather duster
A toad

Rollercoaster
(pages 14/15)

A shopping cart
An abacus
5 barrels
3 brushes
A hammer and spanner
A lantern
A gnome
A tambourine

Pogo Stick

Balloons
(pages 18/19)

An orange
A spanner
A Christmas bauble
2 apples
A basketball
A 10-gallon hat
A noise maker
2 parrots

Sack

Scottish Thistle

Quill

The Earth

Music Box

Refreshments
(pages 20/21)

A bone
A ship
A fly
A spider
A trombone
A flower
An egg
4 strawberries

Lost
(pages 24/25)

4 musical instruments
A pencil sharpener
7 things you look through
Pegasus
2 kings
4 jacks
A dragon
3 keys

Ukulele

Tunnel
(pages 22/23)

A penguin
An owl
A dart
A trowel
A lei
A ukulele
A teapot
A scarf

Funhouse
(pages 26/27)

A gemstone
An ice-cream cone
A wishbone
A pie
A polka dot tie
A tennis racket
A dinner jacket
Santa Claus

Apple

Ostrich

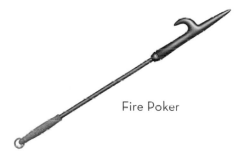

Fire Poker

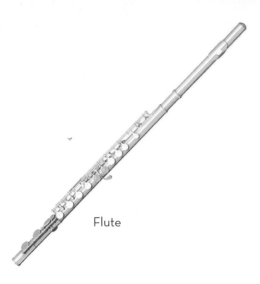

Flute

Seahorse

Walrus

Acknowledgements

We would like to thank the following people:

Everyone at Dynamo for their hard work
Samantha Bryant
Ruby Bryant
Miles Summers
Danielle Casey
Euan Summers
Louis Summers
Meghan Fletcher
Paul Scott
Louise Coulthard
Helen O'Dare
Karen Shapiro
Fizzo Inc.
Sam Grimmer
Peter Tovey
Everyone at Hinkler Books

Sleigh

Typewriter

Bowling Pins

Toucan